To: Wesley, Carson, & Kinsley

Be strong and
be kind always!

♡ Dr. Melinda

The Million Dollar GOAT

The Million Dollar Goat
Copyright 2023 by Melinda G. McCall, D.V.M.
Illustrated by Laraib I. Sukhera

Published by Argyle Fox Publishing | argylefoxpublishing.com
ISBN 978-1-953259-62-2 (Paperback)
ISBN 978-1-953259-82-0 (Hardcover)

Hi! I'm Ernie, a Nigerian dwarf goat. Many people call me the Million Dollar Goat.

I don't have a million dollars though . . .

I'm called the Million Dollar Goat because my bad luck has cost my owner, Sophie Jo, nearly a million dollars!

It all started when Dr. Melinda removed my horn buds. I was just three weeks old.

This kept me from hurting others and getting stuck in the fence.

After Dr. Melinda removed my horn buds,
my head **swelled** up like a balloon.

I also had a **TERRIBLE** headache!
Sophie Jo felt sorry for me, so she held ice
packs on my head to help me feel better.

Dr. Melinda gave me lots of shots
to help make my head stop hurting.

In a few days, I was back to drinking bottles and playing with my brothers and sisters. I felt like a million bucks!

When I was two months old, I started eating grass and plants. One bush with pretty pink flowers looked delicious.

I snuck through the fence for a bite. It was **SO** good! I ate and ate and ate.

A few hours later, my tummy hurt **SO** much.
I got very sick.

YUCK!

Once again, Dr. Melinda saved the day. I stood on her truck's tailgate while she put charcoal in my tummy with a tube.
It was **NOT** fun!
By the next morning I felt like a million bucks!

GOAT DR.

When I turned four months old, I
got really good at goat gymnastics.

One day while finishing a double twist billy goat gruff, I had a rough landing and broke my leg. Sophie Jo was **SO** sad!

Dr. Melinda put a cast on my leg.
She also gave me medicine to help
my leg stop hurting.

Since I was still young, I had to get a new cast in two weeks because my leg was growing **SO** fast.

And after six l o n g weeks,
I was as good as new. I felt like
a million bucks once again!

To protect her favorite goat (that's me),
Sophie Jo brought Bert the guard dog
home. He kept me safe in the pasture, and
we quickly became best friends.

One day, Bert and I were playing together and he got too rough. Bert's ~~SHARP~~ teeth made a big cut on my chest.

Sophie Jo fussed at Bert
and put him in time out!

Dr. Melinda stitched up my cut. She also gave me a shot to get rid of germs inside the cut.

Two weeks later, Dr. Melinda took out my stitches. I was all healed!

Even though I looked like a million bucks, Dr. Melinda said I probably wouldn't be a swimsuit model.

Some folks say, "What doesn't kill you makes you stronger," and I'm proof.

And that's how I became
the Million Dollar Goat.

So If you happen to walk past a wishing well, toss a penny in for your buddy Ernie.

Although I may need more than luck . . .

Printed in the USA
CPSIA information can be obtained
at www.ICGtesting.com
JSHW041938291223
54433JS00005B/36